Make it easy...

English

Age 5-6

Lynn Huggins-Cooper

Rhyming words

Look at this sentence. All the words in bold rhyme. That means they contain the **same sound**. They all end in the letters *at*.

The **fat cat sat** on the **mat**, watching a **bat**!

Draw a line to join each word with its rhyme partner.

a	can	red
b	pink	sack
c	bug	dot
d	bed	stink
e	pot	plug
f	back	fan

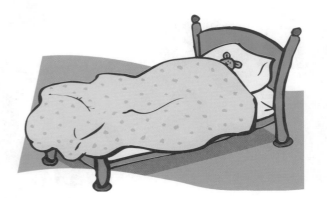

Look in the box to find words that rhyme with each word below. Write the words in the blank spaces.

a yell   _____

b dark   _____

c dog   _____

d box   _____

e win   _____

f sock   _____

g big   _____

fox
frog
pig
smell
rock
bin
park

The alphabet

a b c d e f g h i j k l m n o p q r s t u v w x y z

When people say words are in **alphabetical order** it means they appear in the same order as the alphabet. **A** words come first, then **b** words right up until the end of the alphabet.

> **bat zebra ant** *put into alphabetical order is* **ant bat zebra**.

I Write these letters in alphabetical order.

a f b a d c e g _____

b z x y w v u _____

c p r q t s u v _____

d g f i h k j m l _____

e m l n k j o p _____

f s t v u w r x _____

g d f e h i g j k _____

II Write each set of words in alphabetical order.

a cat   egg   box   _____

b bag   dig   apple   _____

c cup   art   pig   _____

d car   baby   dog   _____

e wall   bed   door   _____

f book   sun   leg   _____

g tree   bird   peg   _____

Spelling simple words

Learning to spell is easy when you use:
look, cover, write, check.

First **look** at the word. Look to see if there are any letters with tails that hang below the line, or sticks that 'stick up' above the line. Try to see the word in your head.

tail y $|$ stick

Then **cover** the word up and try to **write** it. Uncover the word and **check** it. See if you were right. Keep practising!

I Learn these words. Use look, cover, write, check.

a saw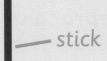

b say

c now

d yes

e did

f not

g was

h but

i run

II Add the missing letter to each word. Use the letters in the box to help you.

a m___n

b f___n

c p___g

d p___n

```
a
i
o
u
```

e d___t ●

f w___g

g s___n

h b___ll

Writing practice

It is important to **write neatly**, so that people can read your writing. Before you start, make sure you are sitting comfortably and you are holding your pencil in the right way between your finger and thumb.

I Trace over these words.

a way   us   to

b too   how   her

c him   old   one

d or   out   saw

e so   not   now

II Copy each word three times.

a see _____ _____ _____

b ran _____ _____ _____

c our _____ _____ _____

d pot _____ _____ _____

e that _____ _____ _____

Full stops and capital letters

A sentence always **starts** with a capital letter and most sentences **end** with a full stop.

It is hot today.
/ \
capital letter   full stop

I **Write these sentences again, adding** capital letters **and full stops.**

a i like you _____

b this is my sister _____

c sausages are my favourite _____

d i am going out _____

e i want to read _____

II **These sentences are mixed up. Write them out in the right order. Use a capital letter and a full stop in each sentence.**

a like brother i my

_____

b dog my walking likes

_____

c smell the cat food can its

_____

d eat we sweets

_____

e wet makes rain you

_____

Names

The name of a **person** or **place** should **start** with a capital letter.

My cat is called **W**iggy.

I come from **B**righton.

 Circle the letters that should be capitals.

a b r i a n

b m r s j o n e s

c a n d r e w

d e n g l a n d

e m r b r o w n

f m i s s l a c e y

g l o n d o n

h m r s m i t h

i f r a n c e

j j a n e t

k d o c t o r d o o l i t t l e

l c a m b r i d g e

m a f r i c a

n s c o t l a n d

 Now underline all of the letters that should be capitals in these sentences. Do not forget to add the full stops!

a my friend jamila comes from yorkshire

b my dog is called bertie

c auntie jane lives in edinburgh

d bruce, stella and jodi are my friends

e we sailed down the river thames

f dad's name is john

g i am going on holiday to portugal with my sister sarah

h i went to durham to see the pantomime cinderella

ff words

Words are made when letters and groups of letters are put together. Learning the way that groups of letters are put together helps you to **build new words**.

$$o + f = of \qquad o + ff = off$$

The two *ff*s sound different to one *f* on its own.

I Look at these letters and groups of letters. Write the words they make in the puffs of smoke.

a flu + ff =

b pu + ff =

c bu + ff =

d cu + ff =

e sni + ff =

f sti + ff =

g mu + ff =

h stu + ff =

i sta + ff =

j whi + ff =

II Write the correct *ff* word next to each picture. Use the words in the box to help you.

muff	cliff	giraffe	puff	whiff	sniff

a _____

b _____

c _____

d _____

e _____

f _____

ll words

Some words end in *ll*. These letters always have a vowel in front of them.

a e i o u

tall

I **Make words using the endings in the ball.**

a b *all bull bill bell*

b y_____

c s_____

d c_____

e h_____

all
ell
ill
ull
oll

f d_____

g f_____

h p_____

i t_____

j w_____

II **Write the *ll* word for each picture.**

a

___ ___ ___ ___

c

___ ___ ___ ___

e

___ ___ ___ ___

b
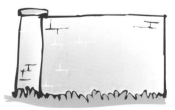

___ ___ ___ ___

d

___ ___ ___ ___

f

___ ___ ___ ___

ss words

Some words end in *ss*.

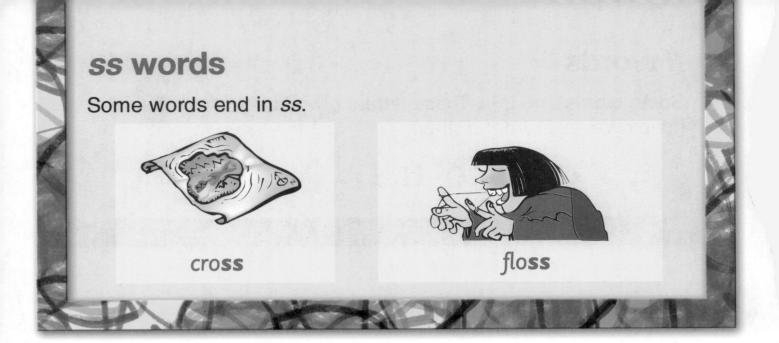

cro**ss**

flo**ss**

I Join the *ss* word to the right picture.

a address

b chess

c pass

d dress

e cress

f floss

II Choose an *ss* word from the box to complete each sentence.

hiss	floss	mess	grass	kiss	cress

a I sat on the _____.

b The mud made a _____.

c I like egg and _____ sandwiches.

d Candy _____ is sweet!

e I _____ my granny.

f The snake went _____.

ck words

In English a word **never starts** with *ck*. But sometimes *ck* is found in the middle or at the end of a word.

ki**ck**ing   ki**ck**

I Draw a picture for each *ck* word.

a clock

b block

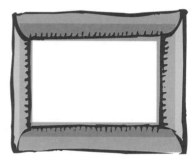

c sock

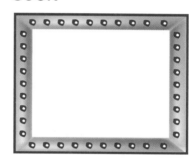

d rocket

e lock

f duck

II *ick* or *ock*? Add the letters to complete the words. Some words can use both – but can you say which ones?

a s_ick   sock_

b kn_____

c w_____

d fl_____

e p_____

f r_____

g l_____

h st_____

i sm_____

j tr_____

11

ng words

The letter blend *ng* never appears at the beginning of words. It is found at the **end** or in the **middle**.

I'm laughing.

I **Circle the words that use *ng*.**

a square rectangle circle

b apple lemon orange

c monkey orangutan ape

d sing laugh shout

e queen prince king

f triangle cymbal drum

g penguin walrus seal

h swing slide roundabout

i necklace ring bracelet

j finger thumb hand

k sting hurt burn

l herring cod eel

II **Write a sentence using each *ing* word.**

a cooking _____

_____

b running _____

_____

c calling _____

_____

d shouting _____

_____

e looking _____

_____

bl words

b and *l* make the letter blend *bl*. Lots of words **start** with *bl*.

blew   **bl**oom

I Tick the words that start with the blend *bl*.

a back dark bland   f bleat bran bill

b black bright big   g burn bleep ball

c baby bin blue   h bloat bunny barn

d blend bark brave   i brand bit bleak

e bus blank broom   j blade brass bust

II Draw a picture for each *bl* word. This will show that you know what it means.

a blade   c blow   e blast

b blink   d blue

cr words

The letters *c* and *r* blend together at the beginning of words to make the sound *cr*.

Draw a line to match each picture to the correct *cr* word.

a crab

b cross

c crisp

d crib

e cress

f crawl

g cry

h crust

Draw a picture that contains each of the things described by these *cr* words.

a crack   b crane   c crazy   d crawl

14

tr words

Lots of words **start** with the letter blend *tr*.

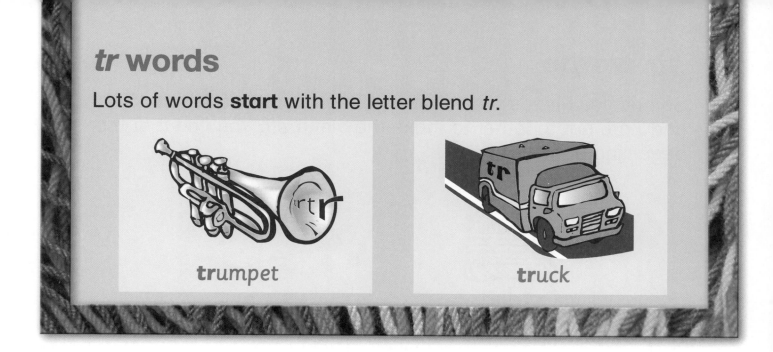

trumpet   truck

 Find the *tr* words in the box below. Then write them down.

take   trade   tick   tramp   trash   table   travel   tray
telly   trip   tank   true   trumpet

a _____   e _____

b _____   f _____

c _____   g _____

d _____   h _____

 Write the correct *tr* words in the spaces.

a I walked down the _____.

b The farmer drives a _____.

c I went to my grandad's house on a _____.

d The fly was caught in the spider's _____.

e When you cross the road, watch for _____.

f The bird made a nest in a _____.

g I always _____ my best.

tree

track

train

tractor

try

trap

traffic

str words

Sometimes blends are made from more than two letters. *S, t* and *r* are put together to make the blend *str*. You find it at the beginning of many words.

string

straw

I Circle the word that begins with *str*.

a strap soft sell

b stall string stink

c strong sand sit

d save street sell

e straw sold saw

f seen so stream

g sick sit stretch

h strange silly smell

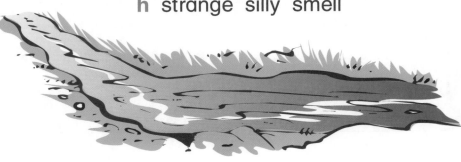

II Now write a sentence using each word you circled.

a _____

b _____

c _____

d _____

e _____

f _____

g _____

h _____

16

nd and lp words

lp and nd are letter blends found at the **end of words**. Like ck and ng, they never appear at the beginning of words.

gulp

wand

I Write *lp* or *nd* to finish each word.

a wi_____

b ki_____

c ba_____

d gu_____

e ha_____

f la_____

g pu_____

h he_____

i fi_____

j sa_____

II Draw a line to match the *lp* and *nd* words to the pictures.

a band   b hand   c yelp   d help   e gulp

Words using *st*

The letters *s* and *t* appear in many words to make the blend *st*.

stamp   po**st**age   po**st**

I Tick the word in each pair that ends in *st*.

a	post	☐	pole	☐	f	bin	☐	bust ☐
b	pick	☐	last	☐	g	trust	☐	take ☐
c	blast	☐	plate	☐	h	make	☐	must ☐
d	fake	☐	fast	☐	i	beast	☐	drink ☐
e	just	☐	jump	☐	j	least	☐	lady ☐

II Choose the correct *st* word, so the sentences make sense. Cross out the word you do not need.

a There was **dust mast** everywhere.

b I used **yeast dust** to make my bread.

c I like history because you learn about the **past crust**.

d The sail flew from the **mast feast**.

e I **must mast** try harder!

f Mum made us a tasty **past feast**.

g I like the **dust crust** on the bread best.

ee words

The letters *ee* together sound like someone is squealing!

I **Draw a line to match each *ee* word to the right picture.**

a sleep

b sheep

c feet

d sleet

e sheet

f beer

g deer

h beep

II **Draw a circle round the *ee* word in each sentence.**

a The water is deep.

b Have you seen my dad?

c Where have you been?

d My sister is a teenager.

e I shall creep up the stairs, because my brother is sleeping.

f Have a peep at these chicks!

g The car horn went beep.

h In the winter we get sleet as well as snow.

oo sounds

oo makes a **special sound**, like an owl hooting.

h**oo**t r**oo**t s**oo**n

I Draw a picture of the missing *oo* words in the boxes below. Use the words in the box to help you.

| stool | pool | food | school |

a The cat sat on the _____.

c The _____ was very noisy!

b Who would like to swim in the _____?

d What is your favourite _____?

II Write the correct *oo* word in each sentence.

a The _____ was bright in the sky.

b The lemonade was lovely and _____.

c I eat yoghurt with a _____.

d Can I come _____?

e _____ is made into jumpers.

too

moon

wool

cool

spoon

20

oa words

There are lots of words that use the letters *oa* together. They make a sound like the name of the letter *o*.

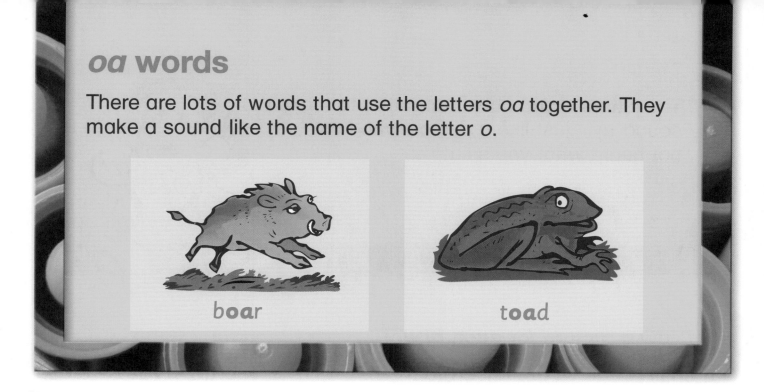

boar   toad

I **Which pictures are *oa* words? Circle the ones you choose.**

a

b

c

d

e

f

II **Draw a line to match each *oa* word to its clue.**

a toast   it sails on the sea

b foal   cars drive on this

c coal   bread

d loaf   baby horse

e oak   it is like a frog

f boat   it burns on a fire

g toad   a hot, cooked slice of bread

h road   tree

ai words

The letters *a* and *i* blend together to make the
sound *ay* – just like a person who has
not heard what you said!

I Draw a picture for each *ai* word.

a snail

c brain

e train

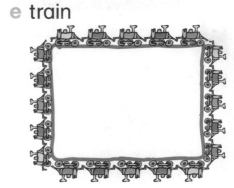

b rain

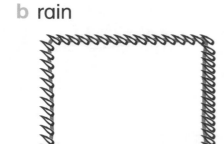

d tail

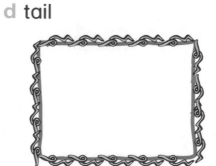

f nail

II Write a sentence using each *ai* word.

a snail   _____

b main   _____

c pail   _____

d fail   _____

e rain   _____

f pain   _____

ie and *y* words

The letter blend *ie* sometimes makes the same sound as the letter *y* when it is at the end of a word – so it can be confusing!

pie

why

I **Which letters are correct? Underline the right answer.**

a pie   py

b tie   ty

c die   dy

d ly   lie

e thyf   thief

f trys   tries

g why   whie

h flie   fly

i cry   crie

j by   bie

II **Complete the words. They all end in *y* or *ie*.**

a d_____

c cr_____

e t_____

b fl_____

d sp_____

Making words

You can **build words** by adding different groups of letters together.

cr + **isp** = crisp

I Add these groups of letters together and write the words you make.

a th + at = __that__

b th + is = _____

c th + en = _____

d wh + at = _____

e wh + en = _____

f wh + ip = _____

g tr + ap = _____

h dr + op = _____

i cr + op = _____

j br + an = _____

II Join together the groups of letters with a line to make words. Use a different colour felt pen for each word.

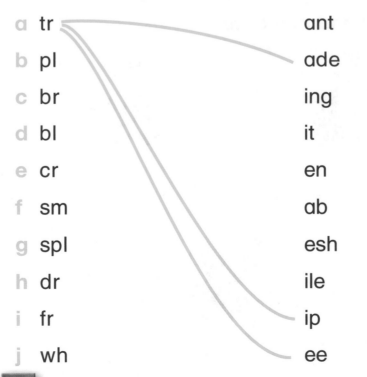

a tr   ant

b pl   ade

c br   ing

d bl   it

e cr   en

f sm   ab

g spl   esh

h dr   ile

i fr   ip

j wh   ee

24

Question marks

Question marks look like this **?**. They are used at the end of a sentence to show it is a question.

Some words give us a clue that a sentence is being asked:

What...?   When...?   How...?
Why...?   Who...?

Where is my hat?

 Add a question mark or a full stop at the end of these sentences.

a Do you like football

b I am glad we are going there

c Can we go now

d May I have one please

e You can play

f This is my dog

g What was that noise

h What time is it

 Write questions of your own using the words what, when, how, why, who. **Do not forgot the question mark!**

a _____

   _____

b _____

   _____

c _____

   _____

d _____

   _____

e _____

   _____

Plurals

Where there is more than one thing, we say it is a **plural**.

To make the word **frog** plural, add an *s*. This shows there is more than one.

one frog

two frog**s**

I   **Circle all the plural words.**

a   The horses eat hay.

b   The birds flew away.

c   Some girls like swimming.

d   The flowers are pretty.

e   Have you seen my comics?

f   These are my favourite sweets.

g   The dogs are barking.

h   Would you like some crisps?

II   **Some plurals do not add an *s*. Join the word to the plural with a line.**

a   woman   mice

b   goose   men

c   mouse   women

d   man   geese

e   louse   lice

In the past

When the **action word** in a sentence ends in *ed* it means the action happened in the past.

> I walk**ed** to school yesterday.

Some words change completely

> I **run** fast changes to I **ran** fast

I Change the action word to the past tense. The first one has been done for you.

a I lik_ed_ the games best.

b I talk_____ to my friend.

c I look_____ at the picture.

d She play_____ with her brother.

e He paint_____ a picture.

f I call_____ my sister.

g They wash_____ their hands.

II Write the correct present tense word next to the past tense word. The first one has been done for you.

a jumped   _jump_

b hopped   _____

c tried   _____

d called   _____

e ran   _____

f lifted   _____

g skipped   _____

h cried   _____

i helped   _____

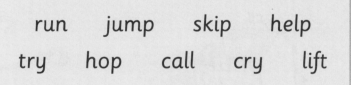

run	jump	skip	help
try	hop	call	cry	lift

Vowels

The letters

a e i o u

are called **vowels**.

Sometimes *y* acts as a vowel in words like 'cry' and 'why'.

Do h**a**ve s**o**m**e** t**e**a.

I Circle the vowels in these words.

a cottage

b seaside

c woods

d babies

e school

f computer

g picture

h doctor

i berries

j leaf

II Fill in the missing vowels to make these words.

a h_____ _____se

c gl_____ss_____s

e c_____k_____

b b_____ _____ks

d m_____lk

f st_____rs

Consonants

Consonants are all the letters of the alphabet except the vowels *a e i o u.*

The consonants are:

b c d f g h j k l m n p
q r s t v w x y z

I Underline the consonants in these words.

a b o a t

b b a b y

c m o u s e

d s a n d

e s u n s h i n e

f d e s k

g p e n c i l

h s c i s s o r s

i e n v e l o p e

j t a b l e

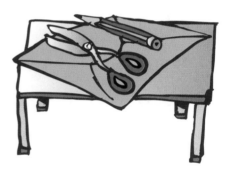

II Write the names of the things under the pictures. Use pairs of consonants in the box to help you.

a

_a_

c

_e_

e

_a_

b

_a_

d

_a_

ct   lg   mn

jm   cn

Same meanings

Sometimes, different words can be used to say the **same thing**.

> shout   yell   roar

These words can all be used to mean someone is talking very loudly.

I   What words mean the same thing? Draw a line to link the matching words.

a	big	run
b	small	blossom
c	shiny	loud
d	noisy	tiny
e	dash	softly
f	gently	seat
g	flower	sparkly
h	chair	huge

II   Think of a word that means the same as these words. Write your word in the space.

a smelly   _stinky_

b sleepy   _____

c jump   _____

d walk   _____

e cry   _____

f sad   _____

g happy   _____

h angry   _____

i wet   _____

j squashy   _____

Opposites

Dark and **light** have opposite meanings.

During the day, it is light.

At night, it is dark.

I **Draw a line to match the opposites.**

a open — shiny

b big — shut

c tidy — horrible

d dull — dry

e hard — soft

f wet — quiet

g loud — messy

h lovely — small

II **Think of a word that means the opposite of each of the words below. Write your words in the spaces.**

a happy _sad_   f full _____

b awake _____   g slow _____

c out _____   h man _____

d up _____   i run _____

e after _____   j low _____

ANSWERS

Page 2
I   a fan   d red
      b stink   e dot
      c plug   f sack

II   a smell   e bin
      b park   f rock
      c frog   g pig
      d fox

Page 3
I   a a b c d e f g
      b u v w x y z
      c p q r s t u v
      d f g h i j k l m
      e j k l m n o p
      f r s t u v w x
      g d e f g h i j k

II   a box, cat, egg
      b apple, bag, dig
      c art, cup, pig
      d baby, car, dog
      e bed, door, wall
      f book, leg, sun
      g bird, peg, tree

Page 4
I   Spellings remembered.

II   a man   e dot
      b fin   f wig
      c pig   g sun
      d pin   h ball

Page 5
I   Words overwritten neatly.

II   Words copied correctly;
rounded letters, correctly
formed, sitting on lines.

Page 6
I   a I like you.
      b This is my sister.
      c Sausages are my
        favourite.
      d I am going out.
      e I want to read.

II   a I like my brother.
      b My dog likes walking.
      c The cat can smell its food.
      d We eat sweets.
      e Rain makes you wet.

Page 7
I   a Brian
      b Mrs Jones
      c Andrew
      d England
      e Mr Brown
      f Miss Lacey

      g London
      h Mr Smith
      i France
      j Janet
      k Doctor Doolittle
      l Cambridge
     m Africa
      n Scotland

II   a My friend Jamila comes
        from Yorkshire.
      b My dog is called Bertie.
      c Auntie Jane lives in
        Edinburgh.
      d Bruce, Stella and Jodi are
        my friends.
      e We sailed down the River
        Thames.
      f Dad's name is John.
      g I am going on holiday to
        Portugal with my sister
        Sarah.
      h I went to Durham to see
        the pantomime Cinderella.

Page 8
I   a fluff   f stiff
      b puff   g muff
      c buff   h stuff
      d cuff   i staff
      e sniff   j whiff

II   a giraffe   d whiff
      b puff   e cliff
      c sniff   f muff

Page 9
I   Children will not know all of
the words below, but they are
given for correctness.
      a ball, bull, bill, bell
      b yell
      c sill, sell
      d call, cell, cull
      e hill, hall, hull, hell
      f doll, dell, dull, dill
      g fall, fill, full, fell
      h pull, pill, pall, poll
      i till, tall, tell, toll
      j will, wall, well

II   a ball   d bull
      b wall   e well
      c bell   f doll

Page 10
I
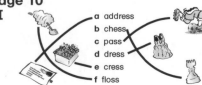
      a address
      b chess
      c pass
      d dress
      e cress
      f floss

II   a grass   d floss
      b mess   e kiss
      c cress   f hiss

Page 11
I   Check child's pictures of each
'ck' item.

II   a sick, sock
      b knock
      c wick
      d flick, flock
      e pick, pock
      f Rick, rock
      g lick, lock
      h stick, stock
      i smock
      j trick

Page 12
I   a rectangle   g penguin
      b orange   h swing
      c orangutan   i ring
      d sing   j finger
      e king   k sting
      f triangle   l herring

II   Any reasonable sentences
containing the words.

Page 13
I   a bland   f bleat
      b black   g bleep
      c blue   h bloat
      d blend   i bleak
      e blank   j blade

II   Check child's pictures of the
words listed.

Page 14
I
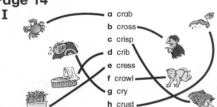
      a crab
      b cross
      c crisp
      d crib
      e cress
      f crawl
      g cry
      h crust

II   Check child's pictures of the
words listed.

Page 15
I   (in any order)
      a trade   e true
      b trip   f trumpet
      c tramp   g travel
      d trash   h tray

II   a track   e traffic
      b tractor   f tree
      c train   g try
      d trap